Just Like Your Daddy!

By: Tiffany Parker
Illustrated by Navi' Robins

Copyright 2021 by Grace + Co.
Illustrations by Navi' Robins

Follow us on social media: @graceandcokids

To my babies:

I hope you continue to brighten up every room you enter. Never dim that light for anyone.
Sienna, Jaxon & Taylor, you are my answered prayers. I can't believe I get to
be your mommy. I love you all the way to the moon and back 10 times!

To Joe:

Thank you for being the most amazing daddy and hero to our crew.
I am forever grateful to do this parenting thing with you, especially when it's
loud and crazy. We all love you real big.

To my dad:

Thank you for setting the bar and raising us with fierce love.
You have always been there. From the ball field to the beauty pageants,
you never missed a beat. Love you pops.

ABOUT THE AUTHOR

Tiffany is a wife and mom of 3 who believes that we have the power to break negative cycles and stereotypes one word at a time. Good daddies do exist. They really do, she is a product of one herself and her children are as well.

This is love letter written to her son filled with daily affirmations to remind him that it's a great thing to be JUST LIKE HIS DADDY!

YOU ARE SO SMART!
YOU ARE SO IMPORTANT!
YOU ARE SUCH A GREAT LEADER TO
YOUR FRIENDS.

JUST LIKE YOUR DADDY.

YOU ARE SO BRAVE!
YOU ARE SO STRONG!
YOU CAN DO HARD THINGS.

JUST LIKE YOUR DADDY.

YOU ARE SO FUN!
YOU ARE SO AMAZING!
YOU LIGHT UP EVERY ROOM YOU
WALK INTO.

JUST LIKE YOUR
DADDY.

YOU ARE SO WONDERFULLY MADE!
YOU ARE SO HANDSOME!
YOU HAVE WHAT IT TAKES TO BE SUCCESSFUL.

**JUST LIKE
YOUR DADDY.**

YOU ARE SO KIND!
YOU ARE SO HELPFUL!
YOUR WORDS ARE SO
POWERFUL.

JUST LIKE YOUR DADDY.

YOU ARE SO COURAGEOUS!
YOU ARE SO CONFIDENT!
YOU NEVER GIVE UP.

JUST LIKE YOUR DADDY.

YOU ARE SO LOVED!
MORE THAN YOU COULD EVER KNOW.

JUST LIKE YOUR DADDY.

I am SAFE.
I am BRAVE.
I am STRONG.
I am BLESSED.
I am WORTHY.
I am ENOUGH.
I am CAPABLE.
I am HEALTHY.
I am DESERVING.
I am CONFIDENT.
I am LOVED.

Made in the USA
Monee, IL
04 November 2024

69071572R00017